Unit Four: Problem Solving

Different Feelings

Think about a time when you were playing with a friend, and you each wanted to do something different. What happened?

In this story, Z doesn't want to do what the kids want to do, so they help Z learn that it's okay to disagree and have different feelings and ideas. When you have a disagreement, you can stop and talk about the problem so you can figure out how to solve it together.

As you listen to the story, pay attention to how Z and the kids feel differently so you can spot their problem.

One rainy morning, Z, Jeremy, and Mia were in the tree house playing with cars and trucks. The sky outside was dark, and every once in a while thunder would rumble loudly through the clouds.

Z didn't really like that noise.

After a while the rain began to slow down and finally stopped. "The storm is over!" Mia cheered.

Z looked at all of the puddles on the ground, and then reached out the window to make sure that the rain had really stopped. A huge wet raindrop fell from a leaf and splashed onto Z's hand!

Z didn't really like that feeling.

"I can't wait to splash in the puddles!" said Mia. "Do you want to play outside with me?"

"Sure!" answered Jeremy. "Let's get our umbrellas in case it starts to rain again. Isn't this going to be fun, Z?"

Z did not agree—Z did not think that this would be fun. The rain was cold and wet and Z did not want to splash in puddles. Z wanted to stay inside where it was warm and dry.

Z saw how excited Mia and Jeremy were to go outside and didn't want them to be mad.

"Okay," sighed Z. "Let's go outside and find some puddles."

Z didn't really like this idea.

Whoops-Z!

Z didn't know that it's okay to disagree with someone.

What would you tell Z to do?

Mia stopped when she noticed that Z looked sad. "What's wrong, Z? Don't you want to go outside?"

"I don't like getting wet," explained Z. "But you and Jeremy want to splash in puddles and I didn't want you to be mad, so I just said okay."

"We wouldn't be upset, Z!" said Mia. "It's okay to say that you feel differently than someone else."

"Really?" asked Z.

Mia nodded. "Jeremy and I don't always agree either, like when he wants to do puzzles and I want to play soccer. When that happens, we just stop and talk to each other so we can figure out how to solve our problem."

Z smiled. "Can we do that now?"

"Okay," said Jeremy, "When we have a problem, the first thing we need to do is to <u>stop</u> and make sure that everyone feels calm before we talk."

Everyone took a deep breath and let it out. They all nodded.

"Next," Jeremy continued, "We need to <u>talk</u> about how each person is feeling so we know our problem. So what's the situation?"

"Well," said Mia, "You and I are excited to go outside in the puddles and play."

"And I want to stay out of the rain," added Z.

"Hmm," said Jeremy. "So our problem is that we don't want to do the same thing."

The kids and Z wondered what they could do to solve their problem so that everyone would feel okay about playing.

Then Mia asked Z if there was anything at all that Z liked about rain. Z thought for a moment. "I like the way the raindrops make things shiny and sparkly. It makes the trees and grass look so pretty."

"And what do you not like about the rain?" Mia asked.

"I don't like to get wet," said Z. "It makes me feel cold and shivery."

Suddenly, Jeremy had an idea. "What if Z put on a raincoat and hat and boots? Then Z could come outside and see the raindrops, but wouldn't get wet. We could all play together!"

Z and Mia thought that this was a great way to solve the problem.

The kids helped Z bundle up in some rain gear. Now Z was nice and warm.

Jeremy and Mia had a great time jumping in puddles, and were careful not to splash Z. Z even tried tiptoeing through a puddle, and thought it was actually a lot of fun when you didn't have to get wet.

The sun finally came out and a beautiful rainbow appeared in the sky, and Z was so happy to be outside with friends to see it.

Z says,
"Whenever we're together my friends help me discover how children on earth get along with each other!"

Z wants you to remember that it's okay to disagree and have different feelings and ideas. When you stop and talk about the problem, you can figure out how to solve it together!

Connecting to the Classroom

➢ **Everyday Moment:** Guide children in identifying the problem when a conflict or difference of opinion occurs, highlighting the different perspectives of those involved.

  ▸ Encourage children to use words to label the problem.

  ▸ Help children practice identifying problems in situations in which they are *not* involved (e.g., *conflicts that are present in children's literature*).

  ▸ Encourage children to take a different perspective.

➢ **Discussions and Activities**

  ▸ Introduce the idea of identifying problems by following the first two of four steps to solving problems:

   ▪ 1) STOP and calm down

   ▪ 2) TALK about the situation and state the problem

  ▸ Discuss why it is helpful to stop, calm down, and talk about the situation when you find yourself in a conflict.

  ▸ Discuss why it is important to share your feelings and ideas, even if you disagree with someone else.

  ▸ Have children role play or use puppets to act out a conflict situation and demonstrate how to stop (and calm down) and talk about the situation and state the problem.

Deciding Together

Have you and a friend ever had to figure out a problem together, like how to share something that you both wanted? How did you decide what to do?

In this story, the kids help Z learn that it's fair to decide things together. That means that everyone gets to share their ideas and everyone listens to each other. Then you can think and decide together on a fair solution that works for everyone.

As you listen to the story, pay attention to the different ideas that Z and the kids have for how to solve their problem, and whether they think of a fair solution.

After a busy day of playing, Z and the kids were working together to clean up the messy tree house.

Z picked up puzzle pieces that were scattered on the floor, and suddenly noticed something small and brown and fuzzy. Z gently picked it up to look more closely.

"What's that, Z?" asked Kayla.

Z held it up as the other kids gathered around.

"It's a caterpillar!" they all shouted.

"Eeewww! I don't like bugs!" said Gabriel. "Let's put it out in the garden."

Kenny disagreed. "If we put it in the garden, it will eat all the plants. We should just smoosh it."

Kayla shook her head. "You can't smoosh it! I want to take it home and put it in my bug house so I can see it all the time."

"Let's hurry up and decide what to do with it before it gets away," said Gabriel.

But Z quickly covered the caterpillar so that none of the kids could see it. "No way!" said Z. "I'm holding it, so I get to decide. I'm going to keep it here with me."

Whoops-Z!

Z didn't know how to decide what to do in a fair way.

What would you tell Z and the kids to do?

"We know that you're holding the caterpillar, Z," said Kenny, "But we should decide together."

"That's right," said Kayla. "We all have different ideas about what to do, so we should stop and talk about it so we can think of a solution that will be okay with everyone."

The kids and Z talked about what they could do. Gabriel thought bugs were icky and didn't want the caterpillar in the tree house. Kenny was afraid to put it in the garden. Kayla was excited to take it home, but Z wanted it to stay in the tree house!

Everyone wondered what to do.

"Hey, Kayla!" said Gabriel. "What if you brought your bug house here? Then the caterpillar would be in its own house instead of crawling around our tree house or the garden. We could keep it here with Z, and you could still see it every day too!" He turned to his friends and asked, "What does everybody think about trying that?"

It wasn't quite what anyone had suggested, but everyone agreed that it was a very fair compromise.

Kayla went home and brought back her bug house, and they all gathered some juicy leaves for the caterpillar to eat. Z and the kids watched the caterpillar and took care of it every day.

One day, Z noticed that the caterpillar looked like it had wrapped itself up inside of a leaf and gone to sleep.

Many days later, Z looked in the bug house again and saw that the caterpillar had come out of its chrysalis—and now it had beautiful wings! It had turned into a butterfly!

The kids and Z decided together that it would be fair to let the butterfly go. As they watched it fly high into the sky, they were all glad that they had done something that made everyone happy—even the butterfly!

Z says,
"Whenever we're together my friends help me discover how children on earth get along with each other!"

Z wants you to remember that when you have different ideas, it's fair to decide together and think of a solution that works for everyone.

Connecting to the Classroom

➤ **Everyday Moment:** Take opportunities to ask children to think of multiple solutions to problems that are presented in stories or actual events.

  ▸ Guide children in thinking about the consequences of different solutions.

  ▸ Encourage children to consider how consequences may vary for the different people involved.

➤ **Discussions and Activities**

  ▸ Discuss why it is helpful to think of multiple solutions to a problem.

  ▸ Discuss what makes solving a problem fair or unfair.

  ▸ Review the steps for identifying a problem:

    ▪ 1) STOP and calm down

    ▪ 2) TALK about the situation and state the problem

  ▸ Introduce the steps for solving a problem once it's been identified:

    ▪ 3) THINK of possible solutions

    ▪ 4)TRY a solution and see how it works for everyone

  ▸ Present hypothetical problems for children to solve using the 4 problem solving steps (e.g., *You are playing a game with a friend. When you go to take your turn, your friend says, "It's my turn!"*).

  ▸ Have buddies design something or complete an activity together that includes challenges (e.g., *Decorate one butterfly with a limited amount of supplies)*, then discuss the successes and challenges of the project and how they decided on solutions together.

Being a Team

What is something that you like to do with friends rather than by yourself? When you play together with others, what are some things that you do to make sure that you are working as a team?

In this story, the kids help Z learn that it is important to cooperate and work as a team. That means that everyone listens to each other and shares and helps one another.

As you listen to the story, pay attention for times when the characters are not cooperating and think about what they could do to work as a team.

One day Z, Gabriel, and Annie spent the afternoon doodling and coloring. Z was drawing pictures of different things from Z's planet, such as gribbles and zorkles. After a while, Gabriel asked the others if they wanted to play with something new.

Z watched curiously as the kids brought out a box full of small, colorful shapes. "What are those?" asked Z.

"These are blocks!" explained Annie. "We use them to build things, like houses and towers and stuff. Do you want to build something together?"

Z bounced up and down excitedly. "Yes! We could build a zanderloo tower like the ones on my planet!"

"Okay!" said the kids. "How do we build one?"

But Z was already zooming around the room, gathering up big armfuls of blocks.

Zip! Zoom! Zip! Zoom!

Z built the zanderloo tower taller and taller.

"Wait, Z!" said Annie. "We don't know how to help!"

But Z was too busy stacking up the blocks and didn't answer.

Annie tried again, "Can we put some blocks on this side, Z?"

But Z kept building the tower.

The kids looked at each other and did not know what to say.

"All finished!" Z shouted proudly, stepping back to admire the tall stack of blocks. "I made a zanderloo tower!"

"That's a cool tower," said Gabriel. "But we wanted to build something together."

"Yeah," added Annie, "That really wasn't very much fun for us, or very fair."

Whoops-Z!

Z didn't understand how to cooperate and work as a team.

What would you tell Z to do?

Z looked around the room and realized that the kids were right. Z had taken almost all the blocks and built the tower alone.

"I'm sorry that you didn't get to build it too," said Z sadly.

Gabriel smiled. "It's okay, Z. We know that you were just really excited and forgot to cooperate."

"What does that mean?" asked Z.

"Cooperating means that everyone listens to each other and works together. If we all want to build something together, we need to work like a team."

"Yes!" said Z. "Let's be a team!"

First, the kids and Z decided what to build together next. Gabriel thought it would be fun to make a train station, and Annie suggested that they build a zoo, but then Z told the kids about the zoobaloot towers on Z's planet. After listening to everyone's ideas, they all decided it would be a lot of fun to build a huge zoobaloot tower together!

Z and the kids worked as a team to build the zoobaloot tower. Sometimes they had to help each other with things they couldn't do by themselves. By cooperating, all the friends were able to work on the tower, and they made one that was much bigger and better than the first one!

Z grinned and said, "I like this tower the best, because we built it together!"

And Annie and Gabriel agreed!

Z says,
"Whenever we're together my friends help me discover how children on earth get along with each other!"

Z wants you to remember that it is important to cooperate when you play and to work together as a team.

Connecting to the Classroom

➢ **Everyday Moment:** Promote cooperation, turn-taking, and teamwork.

  ▸ Set up small group activities and centers with limited materials.

  ▸ Set aside time for small groups to engage in games or activities that have them working toward a common goal.

➢ **Discussions and Activities**

  ▸ Ask children to describe times they cooperate and work together with classmates at school.

  ▸ Discuss what makes working together fair.

  ▸ Have children work in teams to build something out of a given set of supplies (e.g., *a bucket of blocks*). Bring children back together to discuss the strategies they used to cooperate as a team.

  ▸ Have children work in teams to assemble a floor puzzle. Reflect on the teams' successes and ways to improve teamwork.

Z Gets the Ziggles

What is something that makes you feel really excited or loud or wiggly?   What is it like to be around someone else who is very excited or loud or wiggly, when you aren't feeling that way?

In this story, the kids help Z learn that it is okay to have fun, but sometimes it can be too much! That can make it hard for the people around you to play, so it is important to be *considerate* and show that you care about their feelings.

As you listen to the story, pay attention to what Z does to be considerate and calm down when what Z is doing is TOO MUCH for the kids.

One morning when Z woke up, Z had the WIGGLES.

And Z had the GIGGLES.

Z had the ZIGGLES!!!

Z bounced around here.

And Z boinged around there.

And Z laughed and sang as loud as possible!

I AM HAVING SO MUCH FUN TODAY!!!

When Jeremy and Kim arrived at the tree house, Z bounced up and down excitedly. "It's a great day today!"

"It sure is a great day," said the kids. "We're going to play a game—do you want to play too?"

"Maybe later," said Z. "Right now I want to play with trucks!"

As the kids started playing the game, Z began racing trucks back and forth, shouting.

VROOM! VROOM! VROOM!

"It's your turn now," Jeremy said to Kim. But Kim couldn't hear! The kids held their hands over their ears. Z was making *too much* noise!

Whoops-Z!

Z forgot that when you're having fun, it can sometimes be *too much* for everyone else!

What would you tell Z to do?

"Z—that's *too much* noise," said the kids. "We can't hear each other to play our game! Can you please play more quietly?"

"I'll try!" said Z.

Z started playing with the trucks again and tried really hard not to be too loud.

"*Vroom, vroom, vroom.*"

After a while, Z got tired of trucks. Now Z wanted to dance!

Z began to sing and dance and twirl all around the treehouse.

La-la-la-la-la! I love to dance!

Z danced faster and faster and faster!

BUMP!

Z bumped right into the table! The game pieces scattered all over the floor.

Whoops-Z!

Z forgot that when you're having fun it can sometimes be *too much* for everyone else!

What would you tell Z to do?

"Z—that's *too much* dancing around! We can't finish our game now because the pieces are all mixed up. Can you please dance more carefully or dance somewhere else?"

"Okay!" said Z, bouncing up and down and all around.

"Z," said Kim, "I think you have the Ziggles!"

I have the Ziggles! I have the Ziggles!

sang Z loudly.

"Z!" called Jeremy. But Z didn't hear, so Jeremy tried again. "Can we talk to you, Z?"

Z finally stopped bouncing and turned to listen.

"It's okay to have fun or be silly sometimes," said Jeremy, "But right now it's *too much* because it's making it hard for us to hear and to play. When you get too ziggly, it's time to turn it down. That means that you calm yourself down and relax."

"How do I do that?" asked Z.

"When you're feeling really ziggly, you can take some deep breaths in and out—like you're blowing bubbles."

"And when you're feeling really giggly, you can make your voice get quieter…and quieter…and quieter."

"And when your body feels really wiggly—when it feels tickly or jumpy or all squeezed up inside—you can let your body get nice and loose so you can slow down."

"I still feel a little ziggly," said Z, "But this feels so much better now!"

Z and the kids went outside with some bubbles to help Z get the ziggles out. They had so much fun chasing and popping the bubbles together. But then they calmed down and relaxed.

Z took some deep breaths in and out.
Kim laughed more and more quietly…and then just smiled.
Jeremy slowed down until his body was still.

They lay in the grass together and watched the bubbles floating gently above their heads, and it felt very good.

Z says,

"Whenever we're together my friends help me discover how children on earth get along with each other!"

Z wants all of you to remember that it's okay to have fun and be silly. But when it's too much, you can calm yourself down and relax, and that makes playing together a lot more fun for everyone!

Connecting to the Classroom

- **Everyday Moment:** Support children in their daily efforts at self-regulation.

  - Structure classroom space and activities in ways that reduce demands and distractions so children can focus on controlling and adapting their behavior when appropriate.

  - Establish classroom signals (e.g., *palms facing up/down to indicate "turn it up" or "turn it down"*) to provide children with gentle reminders to adjust their behavior, without interrupting their activities.

  - Provide assistance in calming down when children seem overwhelmed.

- **Discussions and Activities**

  - Discuss why is it important to pay attention to the people around you and make sure that you are not making things hard for them when working or playing.

  - Have children practice different ways to calm down.

  - Have buddy pairs play a version of freeze dance in which they "turn up" and "turn down" their actions as you make changes to the volume of the music.